Seeing the Doctor

Building Bridges Series

Building Bridges Series: Seeing the Doctor
Text by Catherine White
Illustrations by Marta Kwasniewska

First published and distributed in 2017 by Gatehouse Media Limited

ISBN: 978-1-84231-178-3

British Library Cataloguing-in-Publication Data:
A catalogue record for this book is available from the British Library

Today, Jamal is not feeling well.

He feels hot.

He feels sick.

He is tired.

His body aches.

He has pains in his stomach.

Jamal says, “I think I need to see a doctor.”
He calls the doctor’s surgery.

“Good morning, Heath Medical Centre,
how may I help you?” a woman says.

“Hello, I feel unwell. I need to see a doctor,”
says Jamal.

“May I have your name and address?” she asks.

"My name is Jamal Abadi.
I live at 23 Manor Road, Heath."

"What is your date of birth?" she asks.
"Twenty-first of July, 1998," answers Jamal.

She tells Jamal to come to the surgery
at 3 o'clock.

Jamal goes to the surgery.

He tells the doctor how he is feeling.

The doctor takes Jamal's temperature.

He looks at his eyes.

He looks in his ears.

He listens to his chest.

He asks Jamal lots of questions.

The doctor says,
“I think you have food poisoning.
You may have eaten some bad food.
Don’t worry, you will soon get better.”

The doctor says to Jamal,
"Go home and rest.
Drink plenty of water.
Eat when you feel up to it,
but try small, light meals at first.
Just eat bland foods like toast, bananas
and rice, until you begin to feel better."

Jamal does as he is told.

A few days later, Jamal is feeling better.
His aches and pains have gone.
His temperature is back to normal.

“I’m feeling hungry,” Jamal says.

“Hmm... what shall I cook for dinner?”

If you have enjoyed this book, why not try another title in the *Building Bridges Series:*

Going to College
Finding a Home
Getting a Job
Going Shopping
Meeting Friends

Gatehouse Books®

Gatehouse Books are written for older teenagers and adults who are developing their basic reading and writing or English language skills.

The format of our books is clear and uncluttered.
The language is familiar and the text is often line-broken, so that each line ends at a natural pause.

Gatehouse Books are widely used within Adult Basic Education throughout the English speaking world.
They are also a valuable resource within the Prison Education Service and Probation Services, Social Services and secondary schools - in both basic skills and ESOL teaching.

Catalogue available

Gatehouse Media Limited
PO Box 965
Warrington
WA4 9DE

Tel/Fax: 01925 267778
E-mail: info@gatehousebooks.com
Website: www.gatehousebooks.com